Carl Fabergé

No. 14   Coronation Box

EASTER EGGS

and

OTHER PRECIOUS OBJECTS

by

Carl Fabergé

A Private Collection of Masterworks
Made for the Imperial Russian Court

The Corcoran Gallery of Art
Washington, D. C.

1961

Foreword

Through the generosity of a good friend of the Gallery, who modestly insists on preserving his anonymity, we now have the welcome opportunity of showing for the first time in this country his superb collection of objects created by Fabergé. These minuscule pieces, which are a delight to connoisseur and layman alike, are fashioned in precious and semi-precious materials of the greatest range and worked in an apparently limitless variety of techniques with a brilliant craftsmanship in designs combining both taste and imagination.

This collection, while smaller in quantity than some, is not surpassed by any in the quality of the individual pieces nor in the richness of its scope and the historic human associations surrounding many of its outstanding masterworks. It has been assembled as a labor of both love and knowledge and with a not inconsiderable amount of detective work. Its creator, in the course of an extraordinarily active life, has found or made the time not only to collect, but also to contemplate and love these exquisite examples of craftsmanship. We are indebted to him for giving us permission to display these treasures here in the Nation's capital where they may be enjoyed by a wider audience.

The number of important collections of Fabergé is not large. On this side of the Atlantic there are those formed by J. P. Morgan, Joseph Pulitzer, Henry Walters, Lillian T. Pratt, and Mrs. Herbert A. May. Among the European collections one recalls especially those of Queen Mary of Great Britain, of the Duchess of Kent, and of Emanuel Snowman, O. B. E., who had an early and leading part in stimulating the collecting of Fabergé after World War I. Perhaps one might even mention the Fabergé cuff-links of Nikita Khrushchev.

The pleasant, if sometimes strenuous, labors which have gone into this exhibition and this catalogue have, in the main, fallen into the enthusiastic and capable hands of several individuals who merit the thanks I am so happy to extend. The first, Miss Cecille Sternberg, *curator ex officio extra urbe in absentio*, to coin a phrase, has given painstakingly effective help to the staff on all aspects of the enterprise. The second, A. Kenneth Snowman, our English collaborator, the author of *The Art of Carl Fabergé* (shortly to be republished in an expanded edition), has been unstinting in making his expert technical knowledge available at all times. He supplied the notes on which this catalogue is based and the perceptive *Foreword*. Gudmund Vigtel, Assistant to the Director, has designed and installed the exhibition and has seen the catalogue through the press with the editorial help of Mrs. Ralph E. Phillips, Curator. We are also indebted to Kurt Wiener, who designed and printed the catalogue, and whose solicitude went much beyond the call of duty.

Credit is due, among others, to Alexander Schaffer of New York for his assistance in forming this collection.

HERMANN WARNER WILLIAMS, JR.
Director

No. 2   Chanticleer Egg

Introduction

SOCIAL HISTORIANS of the future may well wonder how it was that, in the years following the second great World War, the popularity of certain precious objects designed and made by a pre-Revolution Russian craftsman should have increased and spread so prodigiously. The answer is not far to seek. Carl Gustavovitch Fabergé's philosophy was a simple and uncompromising one summed up in the word "quality." It has been said that as much as twenty per cent of his firm's output never left the St. Petersburg workshops where close to two hundred craftsmen worked. Every single article was submitted to Carl Fabergé before completion for his approval, and, if he felt that the work fell short in any respect of the exacting standard he had set, it had to be scrapped and restarted.

This is a far cry from the conditions governing most of the work produced in our day when so much depends upon speed and cost—such a far cry, indeed, that it explains the present nostalgic appreciation for these objects, put together so diligently in Russia at the turn of the Century. They symbolize an age that has gone forever, an age which, for all its obscurantism and bestial injustices, was at least not guilty in its crafts of that debased and anonymous materialism which disgraces our own epoch.

THE FABERGÉS were a French Huguenot family who fled to Russia in the seventeenth century to escape persecution in their own land. They settled in St. Petersburg, and there, in 1846, Peter Carl was born. His father, Gustav, had opened up a business in a small basement four years before as a goldsmith and jeweler. It was this small but successful business that young Carl was to control at the early age of twenty-four. His father had sent him abroad to study, and when he returned to Russia he found himself at the head of a thriving jewelry business and ideally placed to carry out the ambitious projects that had been crystallizing in his imagination.

Fabergé decreed, and in time the entire Russian court meekly obeyed his decree, that in the matter of objects of *vertu* and jewels generally, the emphasis previously placed squarely on sheer value should be shifted to craftsmanship. The sincerity of a gift was to be measured rather by the amount of imagination shown in its conception than by a noisy demonstration of wealth. So he switched from the production of conventional articles of jewelry to the designing of decorative objects composed of materials of considerable beauty, but of no great intrinsic value.

The prestige of his house grew very considerably. He annually designed for the Tsar, as his gift to the Tsarina, the fabulous jeweled Easter eggs which usually contained ingenious surprises. For the King of England, he carried out a series of carvings in various semi-precious stones depicting many of the domestic animals at Sandringham.

Fabergé's flair for selecting the most suitable materials for a particular *objet de luxe* was matched by his cleverness in choosing a craftsman to carry through a specific job for him. His workshop drew on the special skills of craftsmen from many countries—Russia, Finland, Sweden, Germany, and so on — and through his personal genius in combining diverse human elements he was able to create masterpieces which were first and foremost Fabergé. One characteristic which endeared him to his work people was that, once a new man was taken into the shop, he became, right away, a trusted recruit and bore his share, however modest, of both the privileges and responsibilities of the house.

The perfect expression of any particular art form demands the smooth working of the entire technical machinery peculiar to it. Fabergé appreciated this to the full, and in 1900 moved his entire business to one great building where he was able to house, under a single roof, all the most important workshops. Before embarking upon any important new piece, it was his custom to call a round-table conference of all the various specialists who would be required to contribute in some way, at one stage or another, to the final achievement of the job in hand. As the editorial board of a great newspaper meets and confers in order to decide on the "line" to be taken on a specific news item, so the designer of a Fabergé object was given every opportunity of putting his point of view to the men actually entrusted with the task of carrying out his idea. The goldsmith could decide with the enameller exactly how and when his individual work should be done. Almost certainly the gilder would have to consult both these craftsmen—the goldsmith, in order to ascertain the nature and purity of the metal to be used; the enameller, to help him decide on the best color.

The problem of the object or part of the object "going through the fire" for the purpose of soldering, is one of the first importance. Gem stones, for example, cannot be exposed to a flame without a grave risk not readily undertaken by any experienced craftsman. Thus the goldsmith at this prelim-

Upper Left: No. 81; *Upper Right:* No. 46; *Center:* No. 11;
Lower Left: No. 40; *Lower Center:* No. 53; *Lower Right:* No. 51.

inary discussion could plan to solder all the necessary parts, having due regard to the requirements of the setter and the enameller. Each would be able to perform his own particular function at an appointed time, thus obviating any possible danger of clashing. A modern jeweler, reading this, will appreciate how many dismal catastrophes were avoided by this sensible precaution.

The lapidaries working in Russia found everything in their favor. The richest imaginable variety of natural resources was, practically speaking, on their doorsteps, from the vivid Siberian emerald to the grey jasper of Kalgan. This astonishing abundance of mineral deposits found in the Urals, the Caucasus, Siberia and elsewhere in Russia, must have been a source of great satisfaction to Fabergé, and time and time again he has been able to transmit to us his own pleasure in a particularly choice stone in his execution of an animal carving, or a dish or bowl.

With the outbreak of the First World War in 1914 came disenchantment. At the first harsh stab of reality from the outside world, the fairyland of Fabergé melted away—the spell was shattered. The Revolution finally put up the shutters in Morskaya Street. This was the striking of the midnight hour for the House of Fabergé, and the knell having once sounded, the dawn of the following day was to find no time or place for the particular brand of magic that it had distilled so successfully over the years. When the Communists took over control of private business houses, Fabergé is said to have asked, with a characteristic absence of ceremony, for ten minutes' grace "to put on my hat and coat." He died in Lausanne in 1920, an exile both from his country and his work.

T HIS EXHIBITION provides an opportunity to examine at leisure some of the most sensational examples from the House of Fabergé, including no fewer than three of the famous Easter Eggs. In addition, it has the special interest of representing one discriminating collector's choice, his own very personal anthology.

The hand of the St. Petersburg master is detected as surely in a tiny, perfect object such as the simple pale blue enamelled stamp box as it is in the majestic and elaborate Chanticleer Egg, one of the intriging mechanical wonders from Morskaya Street. It is difficult to believe that human fingers have ever fashioned more delicate confections than the two miniature models of sedan chairs, meticulously lined in shimmering mother-of-pearl and enamelled in pastel shades with a consummate skill and refinement.

Consider, too, the gold presentation boxes. These were designed more to impress and dazzle by their pomp than merely to entrance by their charm. Two examples in particular should be singled out for special mention. One is the magnificent *bleu-de-roi* box set with a trellis of diamonds which was made for the lovely Elisabeth Balletta of the Imperial Michel Theatre, a friend of both the Grand Duke Alexis and his nephew, the Tsar of all the Russias, Nicholas II himself. Another important piece, the *Youssoupoff Box*, this time with a musical movement set snugly within the interior, is superbly enamelled *en grisaille* in the best Louis XVI manner.

These are some of the most immediately striking objects in the exhibition, but we must not pass by the exquisitely *ciselé* and enamelled cigarette cases, *bonbonnières*, clocks, miniature frames, hand seals and parasol handles, the cherished accoutrements of Edwardian society.

AS IN ALL GOOD ANTHOLOGIES, there is here in this beautiful collection a distinct and readily discernible bias, in this case in favor of those objects enamelled *en plein* over an engraved or engine-turned background. This is not to say that works in other media are not well represented—indeed, one of the rarest treasures in the collection is the celebrated model of Vara Panina, the gypsy singer, realistically carried out in semi-precious stones. This luckless entertainer's pathetic story is told in the catalogue (no. 91). The vivid and exciting blue of the lapis lazuli coat worn by the charming *Isvoschik* figure is quite unforgettable. A Siberian nephrite watering-can, with red enamelled mounts set with diamonds, is one of the most attractive items in the show; another is the ingenious pair of loving-cups in different colored golds. Each individual visitor will, however, find his or her favorite in this garden of delights.

Fabergé's studies of plants, often set casually in clear rock crystal pots, carved in the round to give the illusion of being filled with water, are as well-known as they are hard to find. These flower pieces are naturalistic, but they are also rigidly selective, and by their crystalline simplicity and clarity of design they escape the banality of the blindly or photographically representational. The *Dandelion "Seed Clock"* shown here is undoubtedly one of the major triumphs in this *genre* and illustrates eloquently how the search for just the right material for the particular job in hand was nothing short of an obsession with Fabergé. We see the same imaginative work in the use of oriental pearls to describe the flowers in a superb little basket filled with lilies of the valley.

This feeling for *matière* is to be seen again and again in the entrancing stone animals and birds. The silvery-black translucent obsidian Bison, so tenderly carved—mat, with the muzzle, horns and hooves brightly polished—is just one extra-ordinary example of the lapidary's craft at the highest level.

These are frankly and unashamedly expensive *objets de luxe*, and, in an age dedicated to the mediocre, whether mass-produced, prepacked or televised, they have an instantaneous and welcome tonic effect on those fortunate enough to be-hold them.

The present writer has not himself seen every piece exhibited here, but he had the joy of examining and handling the great majority of them in their genial owner's lovely home last year. The impact of witnessing the entire treas-ure, carefully set out and documented, must inevitably prove a revelation to every visitor who makes it his business not to miss a unique opportunity.

A. KENNETH SNOWMAN

No. 84 Dandelion "Seedclock"

Brief Notes on Fabergé's Materials and Methods

Fabergé chose his materials for their specific physical properties rather than their intrinsic value. Of the great variety of metals and stones used in his workshop only those examples shown in this exhibition have been included in the following notes.

METALS: Gold in its pure state is far too soft for practical purposes, and it is generally employed in the form of alloys which may vary a great deal in color depending on the metals added to the gold. Fabergé delighted in using golds of various colors in a single object, giving some a dull finish, others a highly polished luster, achieving textures of unusual richness, as in the *Miniature Frame in the Form of a Fire-screen* (no. 6).

Although gold appears to have been his favorite metal, obviously for its great versatility and beauty, Fabergé also exploited the particular characteristics of platinum and silver whenever practical or when esthetic considerations would dictate its use.

STONES: Like metals, the stones were selected with utmost consideration for the job at hand, whether the stone was to adorn some Imperial presentation box or be carved into a charming animal sculpture.

Generally the diamonds used are rose cut which fit in well with the general tonality of an enamelled or plain gold piece. Only occasionally do brilliant cut diamonds embellish Fabergé objects. Sapphires, rubies or emeralds are usually *en cabochon,* i. e., cut in convex shapes, polished but not faceted.

Semi-precious stones were used a great deal, such as moonstone, garnet (a red, glass-like mineral), and olivine (green in color). Other stones found in these objects include rock crystal, jade (a stone cut from two minerals, jadeite and nephrite), bowenite (a mottled green mineral), chalcedony (a quartz with wax-like luster), agate (a variety of chalcedony), jasper (an opaque quartz of various colors), rhodonite (characterized by a warm rose color), obsidian (natural volcanic glass), aventurine (a translucent spangled quartz), chrysoprase (a variety of chalcedony).

Besides the many natural stones, Fabergé frequently used a deep crimson material known as purpurine manufactured through chemical processes in the Imperial Glass Factory.

ENAMELS: Perhaps the most remarkable feature of Fabergé objects is the exquisite enamel work brought to technical perfection and of unique beauty, whether applied in the traditional techniques of *champlevé* (inlaid) and *cloisonné* (enclosed in wire cells) or covering large areas known as *en plein* enamelling.

This last method demands the highest standards of experience and the most exacting control in the firing process and subsequent polishing. The enamel is baked on in several successive transparent layers to the metal ground which may be engraved by hand or may be engine-turned (*guilloché*). The individual layers of enamel may vary in color, producing extraordinary effects of translucency. On occasion transparent and opalescent enamel layers were applied over designs painted in enamel, as for example on the exceptionally handsome *Youssoupoff Box* (no. 18) and the *Circular Bonbonnière* (no. 43).

A characteristic feature in some Fabergé enamels, especially the white, is the rich milky quality obtained by mixing opaque and transparent enamels which produces a lovely opalescent effect.

TECHNICAL TERMS USED IN THE CATALOGUE TEXT

basse-taille—18th century method of inlaying translucent enamel on a concave bas-relief bed

bezel—frame

champlevé—inlaid flush enamel

guilloché—engine-turned

repoussé—surface hammered against a form

rocaille—18th century scroll design — "rock forms"

sablé—rough-surfaced

paillons—spangles—colored foil fixed between layers of enamel

SIGNATURES AND GOLD STAMPS: Fastidious as Fabergé's craftsmen were in their methods of production, the marks of the house were quite often applied in a casual fashion, if at all, sometimes frustrating serious attempts at identification.

The works manufactured in the St. Petersburg workshops generally bear the name Fabergé in Russian characters, ФАБЕРЖЕ, usually preceded or followed by the workmaster's initials. Most of these appear in Roman characters. Often, however, either the workmaster's initials or the firm's name, or both, are left out. Pieces made in the Moscow shops are usually marked with the signature К. ФАБЕРЖЕ beneath an Imperial double-headed eagle or simply stamped with the initials К. Ф. These initials were, however, often applied in the St. Petersburg *atelier* and in other Russian branches of the firm.

Pieces made for the European market were usually signed FABERGE, or C. FABERGE, or C. F. in Roman capitals.

Examples by the following workmasters are presented in this exhibition:

ERIK KOLLIN — mark: E. K.

MICHAEL PERCHIN — mark: M. Π.

HENRIK WIGSTRÖM — mark: H. W.

AUGUST HOLMSTRÖM — mark: A. H.

AUGUST HOLLMING — mark: A∗H

JOHAN VICTOR AARNE — mark: B. A.

ANDREJ GORIANOV — mark: A. Γ.

FEODOR RÜCKERT — mark: Φ. Р.

RUSSIAN GOLD MARKS: The official gold mark for the city of St. Petersburg consisted of two crossed anchors intersected by a scepter until this was abandoned, almost certainly in 1896, in favor of a woman's head in profile wearing a headdress known as a *Kokoshnik*, which has been adopted as the name for this mark. The Moscow hallmark was in the form of St. George and the Dragon until this, too, was changed to the *Kokoshnik* at the same time. Usually the initials of the Inspector at the Hall appear in tiny letters next to the official goldmark.

The Russian gold standards at Carl Fabergé's time were reckoned in alloys of 96 parts corresponding to our 24 parts, or carats—a ratio of four to one. Thus the Russian gold standards of 56 or 72 are the equivalents of our 14 or 18 carats.

No. 3   RED SMALL EASTER EGG CONTAINING A GOLDEN HEN, WHICH CONTAINS A MINIATURE EASEL

Catalogue
of the Exhibition

No. 1 SPRING FLOWERS EGG

1. SPRING FLOWERS EGG: red enamel on gold. The translucent enamel is applied to a *guilloché* field, richly embellished with green carved gold *rocaille* decoration in the Louis XV manner. The rim of red gold which bisects the egg is set with rose diamonds, as are the two surmounting fasteners. When these are parted, the egg opens to reveal the surprise: an exquisite basket of flowers resting on a circular gold plinth. The flowers are carved in milky chalcedony with olivine centers set in green gold; the golden leaves are enamelled translucent green over an engraved ground. The pierced platinum basket is set with a profusion of rose diamonds. The egg is supported by a carved and fluted circular bowenite base mounted with scrolls and chased acanthus leaves in red and green gold and set with rose diamonds.

Made between 1885 and 1891, this Imperial Easter Egg was presented to Marie Feodorovna by her husband, Tsar Alexander III. Like all the early eggs, this example is smaller than those made after 1895. The flower basket motif was used again much later by Fabergé in his *Winter Egg* of 1913.

SIGNED: M. П.

GOLD MARK: crossed anchors

HEIGHT OF EGG: 3″

HEIGHT OF BASKET: $1\frac{5}{16}$″

2. CHANTICLEER EGG: translucent ultramarine enamel on a shimmering *guilloché* surface of gold. Heavy laurel swags carved in green gold hang from a circular grille in pierced gold at the top of the egg. A line of pearls within borders of leaves and berries carved in green gold forms a belt around the center of the egg. The belt is interrupted by the opalescent white enamelled clock dial set in red gold and rimmed by pearls. The hands are of gold and the numerals are painted in blue enamel. The egg is mounted on a four-sided pedestal decorated with symbols in red and green gold of the arts and sciences. The four concave main panels of the base are enamelled translucent ultramarine and the alternating lesser panels, as well as the fluted shaft supporting the egg, are in opalescent white.

At each hour the grille at the top of the egg opens and a diamond-set rooster in gold and vari-colored enamels rises automatically from the interior, crowing and flapping its wings. When it has announced the time, the bird disappears beneath the grille which closes down over the egg.

The Chanticleer Egg was probably presented to the Dowager Empress Marie Feodorovna in 1903 by Nicholas II.

SIGNED: M. П.

GOLD MARKS: 56 and *Kokoshnik*

HEIGHT: 11″

3. **SMALL RED EASTER EGG, 1898:** red translucent enamel on engraved gold. The rim which divides the egg is set with rose diamonds and two large portrait diamonds covering the initials B. K. and the year 1898. The yolk in opaque enamel conceals a gold hen in vari-colored enamels set with rose diamond eyes; the hen in turn contains a folding easel surmounted by a heart-shaped diamond and a cabochon ruby. The easel carries a bevelled rock crystal framed by rose diamonds. The original miniature which it once contained is now missing.

This Egg was presented by Alexander Ferdinandovitch Kelch to his wife, Barbara Kelch, a wealthy eccentric and an important patron of the House of Fabergé.

SIGNED: M. Π.
GOLD MARK: crossed anchors
HEIGHT: $2\frac{1}{4}''$

MINIATURE REPLICAS

4. **COLUMN:** red and green gold set with rose diamonds. The column is decorated with husks and berries, laurel wreaths, swags and Vitruvian scrolls carved in gold. The top is surmounted by a Romanoff double-headed eagle in green gold above a gold sun-in-splendor. A small hook indicates that the column originally carried a miniature portrait. The column is supported by a square base on four reeded bun feet.

SIGNED: H. W.
HEIGHT: $6\frac{3}{16}''$

5. **MINIATURE FRAME ON A COLUMN:** red and green gold frame on a royal blue translucent enamelled support. The column, enamelled *en plein* over a wave-patterned field, is decorated with Louis XVI motifs of swags, wreaths, diamond-set bows, and a quiver of arrows traversing a flaming torch. It is supported by a square base with four lion-paw feet.

SIGNED: M. Π.
HEIGHT: $5\frac{5}{8}''$

6. **TWO-SIDED MINIATURE FRAME IN THE FORM OF A FIRE SCREEN:** gold in five colors with white and rose enamel. The screen is adorned with chased gold floral swags and trophies with a framework enamelled in opaque white *champlevé* and set with two oriental pearl finials. The screen is enamelled opalescent white over a scalloped ground with an oval photograph of Nicholas II framed with half-pearls. The reverse carries a photograph of the Tsarina similarly framed against an enamelled background in opalescent rose.

SIGNED: H. W.
GOLD MARK: 72
HEIGHT: 7″
WIDTH: $3\frac{3}{4}''$

No. 6   Two-sided Miniature Frame in the form of a Fire Screen

No. 7
Louis XVI Cabinet

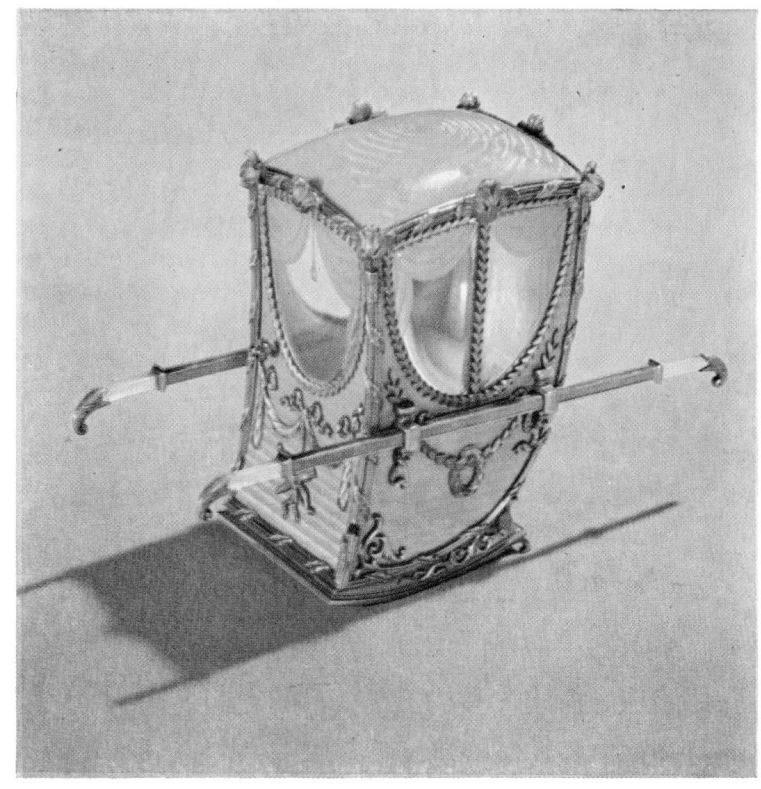

No. 8 Sedan Chair

7. LOUIS XVI CABINET: dark brown agate and carved red, green and yellow gold. The cabinet is decorated with plaques which are enamelled translucent sepia on backgrounds of engraved parallel lines with painted classical motifs in dark sepia. The hinged top is set with an engraved rock crystal panel.

   Signed: M. Π.
   5¼″ x 3⁷⁄₁₆″ x 1⁷⁄₈″

8. SEDAN CHAIR: engraved red gold enamelled translucent pink. The panels of the chair are enamelled on a *moiré guillochage* with mounts in mother-of-pearl and carved green gold. The windows are of engraved rock crystal and the interior is lined with engraved mother-of-pearl.

   Signed: H. W.
   Height: 3″

No. 9
Sedan Chair

9. SEDAN CHAIR: engraved red gold enamelled translucent rose. The panels are enamelled on sun-ray backgrounds with symbols of the arts painted in sepia. The *sablé* borders are enamelled opaque white and translucent emerald green with mounts carved in yellow gold. The windows are of engraved rock crystal, and the interior is lined with mother-of-pearl.

SIGNED: M. П.
GOLD MARK: 72
HEIGHT: $3\frac{5}{8}''$

10. REPLICA OF THE STATUE OF PETER THE GREAT BY ÉTIENNE MAURICE FALCONNET: statue in vari-colored golds supported by a carved emerald.

SIGNED: M. П.
HEIGHT: $1\frac{3}{4}''$
LENGTH: $2''$

11. WATERING-CAN: Siberian nephrite with an engraved gold handle enamelled translucent red and a gold spout set with rose diamond mounts. Originally from the collection of Mme. Elisabeth Balletta of the Imperial Michel Theatre.

HEIGHT: $1\frac{1}{2}''$
LENGTH: $4\frac{1}{4}''$

IMPERIAL BOXES

12. IMPERIAL PRESENTATION BOX: dull green gold enamelled translucent salmon and set with diamonds. The enamel is applied over a *guilloché* ground in sun-ray and wave patterns and is embellished with carved *rocaille* scrolls set with diamonds. The diamond monogram of Nicholas II within an oval border of diamonds adorns the center of the lid.

SIGNED: M. П.
$4''$ x $2\frac{5}{8}''$ x $1\frac{1}{2}''$

13. IMPERIAL PRESENTATION BOX: gold set with diamonds. The center of the lid is adorned with a raised oval medallion showing the Imperial eagle which is carved in relief and set with diamonds. The eagle is surrounded by a band of rose diamonds and surmounted by a crown. The lid, on either side of the central design, is decorated with foliate sprays and with borders in two-colored gold with touches of white enamel and rose diamonds at the corners. The sides are similarly decorated in gold of two colors. This box was presented in 1897 to the French Chief of Protocol, General Molard, during the first visit of Tsar Nicholas II to France.

SIGNED: M. П.
$3\frac{5}{8}''$ x $2\frac{5}{16}''$ x $1\frac{1}{4}''$

No. 18 Youssoupoff Box

14. CORONATION BOX: red gold enamelled translucent yellow on fields in sun-ray and wave patterns. The borders are decorated with husks carved in green gold. A diamond-set trellis with Romanoff double-headed eagles enamelled opaque black is mounted on the lid, which is centered by the Imperial cipher of Nicholas II in diamonds against a sun-ray background with oyster-colored opalescent enamel.

This box was given by the Tsarina to her husband on Easter Day, 1897, the day he presented her with the *Coronation Egg*.

SIGNED: A. H.

GOLD MARK: crossed anchors

$3\frac{5}{8}''$ x $2\frac{9}{16}''$ x $\frac{15}{16}''$

15. ANTIQUE FRENCH SNUFFBOX, 1777: engraved red gold and translucent red enamel. The box is further decorated with opaque white and translucent green and scarlet enamel. The lid is set with a panel of an allegorical scene painted in enamel. This and the following object were originally in the Hermitage Collection.

SIGNED: J. E. B. (Joseph Étienne Blerzy)

PARIS GOLD MARK

$3\frac{1}{4}''$ x $2\frac{3}{8}''$ x $1\frac{15}{16}''$

16. SNUFFBOX: engraved red gold and translucent green enamel. The lid is set with an allegorical scene painted in *grisaille* enamels on a panel edged with rose diamonds. The borders are decorated with opalescent beads and translucent green and red enamel.

This snuffbox is a pastiche based on the *Antique French Snuffbox* (no. 15) and is said to have been manufactured by Fabergé in answer to the Tsar's challenge that he match the skill of the 18th century French goldsmiths. It was exhibited in the Hermitage by order of the Tsar.

SIGNED: M. П.

GOLD MARKS: 72 and crossed anchors

$3\frac{1}{4}''$ x $2\frac{9}{16}''$ x $1\frac{5}{16}''$

17. CIRCULAR IMPERIAL PRESENTATION BOX: gold-mounted and enamelled translucent grey-blue. The enamel of this box is applied to a *guilloché* ground and is decorated with eight carved Romanoff double-headed eagles. The lid is set with a gold coronation medal with profile portraits in *bas-relief* and the legend: *Emperor Alexander III and Empress Marie Feodorovna, Coronation in Moscow 1883*. The reverse side features a Romanoff eagle with the words: *God is with Us*.

SIGNED: M. П.

GOLD MARK: crossed anchors

HEIGHT: $1''$

DIAMETER: $2\frac{1}{8}''$

MUSIC BOX

18. YOUSSOUPOFF BOX: gold enamelled opalescent pale sepia. The rectangular box with chamferred corners features painted panels of six palaces owned by the Youssoupoff family. The lid shows the Archangelskoe Palace and the front panel the Residence on the Moika Canal in St. Petersburg where Rasputin was put to death by Felix Youssoupoff, one of the two sons whose initials appear on this box. The pictures on the lid and bottom are painted in enamel over a sun-ray pattern; the others are painted over a background of parallel lines. The borders are made up of opalescent enamel beads and translucent emerald leaves on *sablé* paths. The initials of Felix and Zénaïde and their two sons, Nicholas and Felix, are painted beneath Imperial crowns at the four corner panels. The diamond thumb piece is formed in the numerals XXV.

This box was presented to the Prince and Princess Youssoupoff on their twenty-fifth wedding anniversary.

SIGNED: H. W.

GOLD MARK: 72

$3\frac{1}{2}''$ x $2\frac{5}{8}''$ x $1\frac{3}{4}''$

VANITY BOX

19. VANITY BOX: engraved gold with blue enamel. The lid of the box is trellised with a pattern of rose diamonds and displays the initials of Madame Balletta. The sides are decorated in Louis XV *basse-taille* technique with sapphire blue floral swags. The box is still kept in its original jeweller's case.

This piece was designed for Madame Balletta at the order of the Grand Duke Alexis whose initials and anchor cipher appear on the bottom of the box.

SIGNED: H. W.

$4''$ x $2\frac{3}{4}''$ x $1''$

CIGARETTE BOXES AND CASES

20. CIGARETTE BOX: silver-gilt and opalescent pink enamel. The *en plein* surfaces are engraved with a *moiré* pattern and the flanges bordered by lines in opaque white enamel.

SIGNED: A. H.

$3\frac{11}{16}''$ x $2\frac{3}{16}''$ x $1\frac{7}{16}''$

21. CIGARETTE BOX: gold enamelled translucent royal blue. The enamel is applied to an engraved scallop-patterned field with the borders enamelled opaque white and translucent red and green with opalescent white beads on gold *sablé* paths. The thumb piece is set with rose diamonds.

SIGNED: H. W.

GOLD MARK: 72

$3\frac{3}{4}''$ x $2\frac{1}{2}''$ x $\frac{11}{16}''$

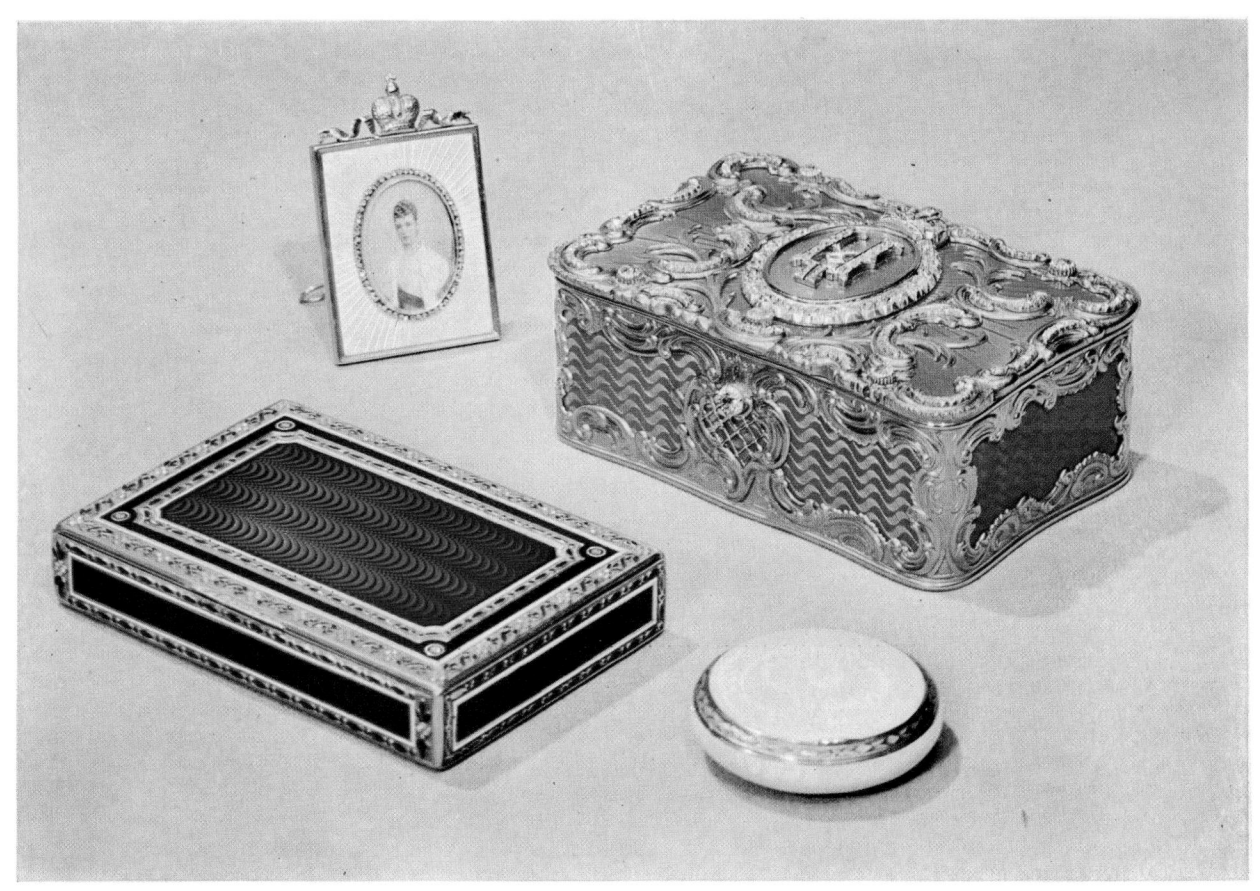

Upper Left: No. 83; *Upper Right:* No. 12; *Lower Left:* No. 21; *Lower Right:* No. 36

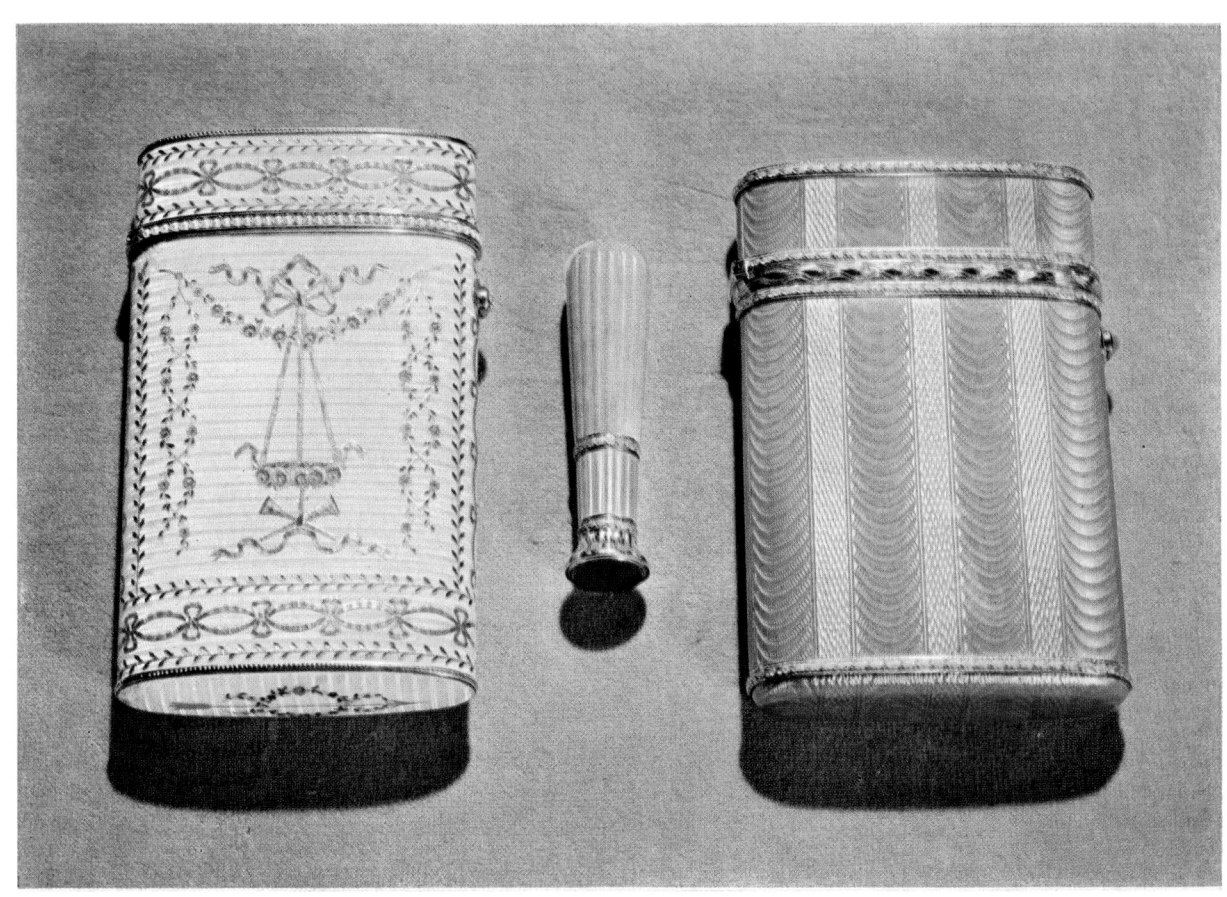

Left: No. 27; *Center:* No. 61; *Right:* No. 26

22. CIGARETTE CASE: silver-gilt enamelled translucent yellow over a *moiré guillochage* with a rose diamond thumb piece.

This case was made for the English market as evidenced by the high silver mark 925 and the initials C. F.

SIGNED: H. W.

$3\frac{5}{16}''$ x $2''$ x $\frac{9}{16}''$

23. CIGARETTE CASE: silver and translucent blue enamel on a sun-ray patterned ground with carved gilt laurel mounts. The thumb piece is set with rose diamonds.

SIGNED: H. W.

$3\frac{3}{8}''$ x $1\frac{13}{16}''$ x $\frac{9}{16}''$

24. CIGARETTE CASE: rose pink enamel over a wavy *guilloché* ground. The case, of flattened tubular shape, is decorated at each end with chased gold husk borders.

SIGNED: A. H.

LENGTH: $3\frac{3}{8}''$

25. TUBULAR CIGARETTE CASE: silver-gilt enamelled translucent mauve. The *en plein* enamel covers a *guilloché* wavy field with two red and green gold laurel mounts. The case is equipped with a rose diamond thumb piece.

SIGNED: A. H.

$3\frac{1}{2}''$ x $1\frac{5}{8}''$ x $1\frac{3}{8}''$

26. CIGARETTE CASE: translucent green enamel on a *guilloché* pattern of swags. The case, decorated with mounts in red and green gold and a wavy flange in the 18th century manner, has a moonstone push piece.

$3\frac{3}{4}''$ x $2\frac{1}{2}''$ x $\frac{3}{4}''$

27. CIGARETTE CASE: red gold enamelled opalescent white over a wavy engraved ground. Elaborately decorated with colored *paillons* in the technique of Jean Coteau and carried out in the manner of Sallembier, the case is set with a border of half-pearls and a brilliant diamond push piece.

SIGNED: M. П.

$4''$ x $2\frac{5}{8}''$ x $1\frac{3}{16}''$

28. CIGARETTE CASE: silver-gilt enamelled translucent royal blue on a swag patterned *guillochage*. The case, rectangular and of a flattened oval section, is mounted with engraved line-and-dot bands and an elaborate path of leaves carved in dull green gold over a background of opaque white edging the hinged lid. It is set with a large rose diamond push piece.

SIGNED: H. W.

$3\frac{5}{16}''$ x $2''$ x $\frac{5}{8}''$

29. C I G A R E T T E   C A S E : red and green gold alternating in a ribbed wave pattern. The thumb piece is set with a cabochon sapphire.

    Signed: H. W.

    $4\frac{3}{8}''$ x $2\frac{5}{8}''$ x $\frac{11}{16}''$

30. C I G A R E T T E   C A S E : gold in a reeded design. The case has a cabochon sapphire thumb piece.

    Signed: H. W.

    $3\frac{13}{16}''$ x $2\frac{3}{4}''$ x $\frac{5}{8}''$

31. C I G A R E T T E   C A S E : carved Siberian nephrite. Of flattened oval form, the case is equipped with three diamond "frost" mounts serving as hinges and clasp. This particular motif was a favorite theme of Dr. Emanuel Nobel for whom the case was designed. Dr. Nobel was a nephew of the Swedish inventor, Alfred Nobel.

    Signed: FABERGE

    $3\frac{1}{2}''$ x $1\frac{13}{16}''$ x $1\frac{1}{16}''$

32. C I G A R E T T E   C A S E : silver-gilt enamelled translucent pink on a *moiré guillochage* with carved gilt laurel mounts and a diamond-set thumb piece.

    Signed: A. H.

    $3\frac{1}{2}''$ x $1\frac{13}{16}''$ x $\frac{1}{2}''$

33. C I G A R E T T E   C A S E : bowenite with a gold bezel enamelled with opalescent beads and translucent red *cloisons* of diamond-shape and set with a pearl thumb piece. The lid is embellished with an opal relief carving of the Tsarina and her two daughters, the Grand Duchesses Olga and Tatiana. The portraits are surrounded by an elaborate leaf design surmounted with a Romanoff eagle.

    Signed: M. П.

    Gold mark: crossed anchors

    $3\frac{3}{4}''$ x $3''$ x $\frac{15}{16}''$

POWDER BOXES

34. P O W D E R   B O X : silver-gilt enamelled opalescent white on a swag patterned ground. The box has carved gilt laurel borders and a rose diamond thumb piece. The lid is mounted with an oval plaque of moss-agate edged with rose diamonds.

    Signed: H. W.

    $2\frac{1}{2}''$ x $1\frac{3}{4}''$ x $\frac{7}{16}''$

35. C I R C U L A R   P O W D E R   B O X : gold enamelled with a linear pattern of black stripes. The borders are enamelled translucent rose over a *guilloché* ground. The medallions mounted on the top and bottom of the box are enamelled in a similar manner and are applied with

No. 16 SNUFFBOX

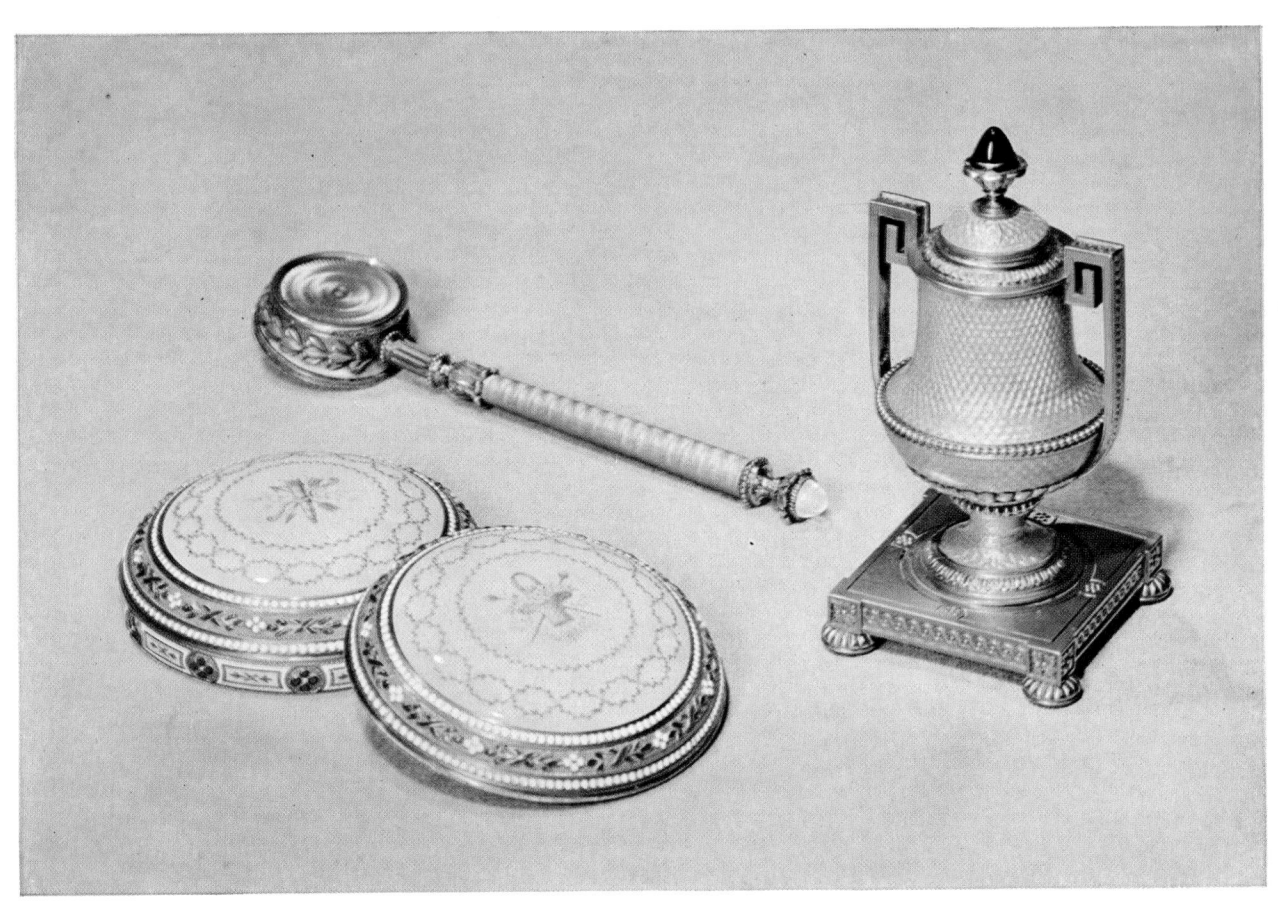

Left: No. 43; *Center:* No. 60; *Right:* No. 49

FORTY

a vase of flowers and a single flower in rose diamonds, respectively. The hinged lid is set with
a mirror and conceals an inner gold lid designed
to keep the powder air-tight.

SIGNED: H. W.

GOLD MARK: 72

DIAMETER: $1\frac{7}{16}''$

36. CIRCULAR POWDER BOX: enamelled
opalescent white on an engraved field. The box
is decorated with mounts of red and green gold.

SIGNED: К. ФАБЕРЖЕ

DIAMETER: $1\frac{3}{4}''$

37. CIRCULAR PATCH BOX: translucent
mauve enamel over a *guilloché* ground. The
lid of the box is set with a rose diamond and
mounted with a mirror on the inside. The interior is in silver-gilt.

SIGNED: К. ФАБЕРЖЕ

DIAMETER: $1\frac{3}{4}''$

BONBONNIÈRES

38. OCTAGONAL BONBONNIÈRE: gold
enamelled translucent mustard yellow on a
ground engraved in a sun-ray pattern. The
hinged lid and flange are set with borders of
rose diamonds. The lid is mounted with an
oval miniature framed with rose diamonds of a
young girl after Greuze.

Originally in the Balletta Collection.

SIGNED: M. П.

HEIGHT: $\frac{13}{16}''$

WIDTH: $1\frac{7}{16}''$

39. HEXAGONAL BONBONNIÈRE:
gold enamelled opalescent white on a ground
engraved in wave patterns. The hinged lid is
formed of a single carved opal edged with rose
diamonds.

Originally in the Balletta Collection.

SIGNED: M. П.

HEIGHT: $\frac{7}{8}''$

WIDTH: $1\frac{3}{8}''$

40. SEMI-CIRCULAR BONBONNIÈRE:
carved rock crystal. The gold bezel is enamelled opaque white and set with a square cut
ruby at either corner. The hinged lid is engraved with a swag design and equipped with
a thumb piece composed of a triangular ruby
and rose diamond cluster.

SIGNED: FABERGE

HEIGHT: $\frac{7}{8}''$

WIDTH: $2\frac{1}{2}''$

41. OCTAGONAL "TSAR KOLOKOL" BONBONNIÈRE: silver-gilt and enamel. The cover shows "Tsar Kolokol" (see below) in enamels. The sides and narrow borders are brilliantly enamelled with floral designs. The center of the base is enamelled with a spray of pansies.

> SIGNED: Ф. Р.
> HEIGHT: $\frac{7}{8}$″
> WIDTH: $1\frac{1}{2}$″
> NOTE: During a fire in 1737 "Tsar Kolokol", the King of Bells, weighing 150 tons, fell to the ground and a large fragment broke off, making a hole large enough for three horses to pass through. The bell was raised to a platform by the combined efforts of hundreds of soldiers. It now stands as an ancient monument near the Bell Tower of Ivan the Great inside the Kremlin.

42. OVAL BOX: red gold. The box is engraved with sun-ray patterns and is decorated with pellets in the Louis XVI manner. The borders of green gold are chased with laurels.

> SIGNED: M. П.
> $1\frac{5}{8}$″ x $1\frac{5}{16}$″ x $\frac{7}{8}$″

43. CIRCULAR BONBONNIÈRE: gold enamelled opalescent pale flame with painted motifs in sepia enamel. The motifs are bordered by gold *sablé* paths with beads enamelled opaque white and floral and ribbon decorations in red and green translucent enamel.

> SIGNED: H. W.
> GOLD MARK: 72
> DIAMETER: $2\frac{3}{16}$″

44. CIRCULAR BONBONNIÈRE: gold enamelled translucent grey on a *guilloché* field bordered by lines in opaque white enamel. The lid and bottom of the box are adorned with rosettes carved in green gold on a red *sablé* ground. The wall of the lid is decorated with a *ciselé* leaf and berry meander design in green gold on a red *sablé* path.

> SIGNED: H. W.
> GOLD MARK: 72
> HEIGHT: $\frac{13}{16}$″
> DIAMETER: $1\frac{15}{16}$″

BOWL

45. CIRCULAR BOWL: purpurine mounted with gold. The bowl is carved from a single piece of purpurine and mounted with a red gold bezel with a laurel border and swags carved in green gold.

> SIGNED: M. П.
> GOLD MARK: crossed anchors
> DIAMETER: $3\frac{7}{8}$″

DRINKING CUPS

46. DOUBLE MARRIAGE CUP: gold in four colors. The four facets of the fluted stems are each in a different shade of gold; the two bowls are similarly varied and engraved. The cups are held together by means of a bayonet fitting.

    SIGNED: M. Π.

    TOTAL HEIGHT: $3\frac{9}{16}''$

47. VODKA CUP: silver-gilt enamelled translucent deep red on a diapered wave pattern. The rim is enamelled *champlevé* with translucent green leaves and beads in opaque white.

    The cup is unsigned; the silver mark dates the cup prior to 1896.

    HEIGHT: $1\frac{5}{8}''$

GLUE POTS

48. GLUE POT: bowenite mounted with gold. The pot, decorated with swags and bows in varicolored gold, is supported by three lion-paw feet of gold. The gold bows and the brush handle are set with rubies.

    SIGNED: M. Π.

    HEIGHT: $2\frac{5}{8}''$

49. GLUE POT: silver-gilt enamelled translucent pale green on a *guilloché* field. The brush is set with a cabochon garnet finial.

    SIGNED: B. A.

    HEIGHT: 3''

50. ROUND GLUE POT: gold enamelled red over a wavy *guilloché* field. The brush has a cabochon chalcedony finial in a gadrooned gold mount.

    SIGNED: H. W.

    DIAMETER: $1\frac{3}{4}''$

SCENT FLACONS

51. OVAL SCENT FLACON: translucent pale blue enamel on an engraved ground. The hinged lid, surmounted by a half pearl, is mounted with a red gold bezel with a laurel collar in green gold. The bottle is fitted with a fluted gold stopper.

    SIGNED: M. Π.

    HEIGHT: $1\frac{7}{8}''$

52. MINIATURE EASTER EGG SCENT FLACON: enamelled light blue. The top of the flacon, which is fitted with a loop for suspension, is decorated with leaves carved in two-

colored gold. Rose diamonds are set below these with pendant swags of laurel leaves. The base is decorated with leaves and a moonstone.

SIGNED: H. W.

HEIGHT: 1⅜″

SEALING WAX HOLDER

53. SEALING WAX HOLDER: red gold with white stripes in opaque enamel and mounted with chased green gold bands in meander patterns.

SIGNED: M. Π.

LENGTH: 3⅞″

STAMP BOX

54. STAMP BOX: enamelled translucent pale blue on a *guilloché* ground and mounted in gold of two colors.

SIGNED: H. W.

1⅛″ x 15/16″ x ½″

BODKIN CASE

55. BODKIN CASE: enamelled in the Rothschild colors, translucent yellow and royal blue on *guilloché* backgrounds.

SIGNED: M. Π.

LENGTH: 3⅞″

PARASOL HANDLES

56. CYLINDRICAL PARASOL HANDLE: enamelled pink over a *guilloché* ground. The sides of the handle are set with interlacing wreaths and emeralds divided by opaque white enamelled borders and bands of rose diamonds. The top is decorated with a wreath border and translucent pink enamel centered by an emerald within a rose diamond cluster.

From the collection of the Duchess of Kent.

HEIGHT: 3⅛″

57. TUBULAR PARASOL HANDLE: enamelled opalescent white on a field in swag pattern. The handle is mounted with two red gold collars embellished with laurel leaves carved in green gold.

HEIGHT: 3″

58. PARASOL HANDLE: the shaft, enamelled opalescent white, carries a gold trellis set with rubies which rises to a magnificent cushion-cut Siberian amethyst.

The signature indicates that this object came from Fabergé's Moscow branch.

SIGNED: K. Φ.

HEIGHT: 2½″

Upper Left: No. 73; *Upper Center:* No. 104; *Upper Right:* No. 38; *Center:* No. 74;
Lower Left: No. 10; *Lower Center:* No. 39; *Lower Right:* No. 19

59. SHEPHERD'S CROOK PARASOL HANDLE: the curved handle is of Siberian jade set with a red gold mount which is decorated with laurel leaves carved in green gold. The shaft is enamelled translucent red on a ground of barley pattern and overlaid with sloping stripes in opaque white enamel.
   SIGNED: H. W.
   HEIGHT: 4⅛″

HAND SEALS

60. HAND SEAL: red and green gold enamelled translucent pale mauve on a *guilloché* ground. The handle is set with a moonstone finial. The white chalcedony sealing stone is engraved with the initials of the original owner, Queen Victoria of Spain.
   SIGNED: H. W.
   LENGTH: 4¼″

61. AVENTURINE HAND SEAL: fluted aventurine quartz with matching gold mounts and decorated with a silver collar enamelled translucent pale green between laurel bands in red and green gold. It is set with a cornelian sealing stone.
   SIGNED: M. Π.
   HEIGHT: 2⅜″

62. JADE HAND SEAL: Siberian nephrite with engraved and fluted red gold mount, with laurel decorations in green gold, and a collar of translucent red enamel on a *guilloché* field.
   SIGNED: M. Π.
   HEIGHT: 3¾″

63. LAPIS LAZULI HAND SEAL: the foot is enamelled with three panels in opalescent pale sepia against a background of engraved trophies framed with lines in opaque white enamel. The seal is embellished with two rings of rose diamonds and set with a lapis lazuli sealing stone.
   HEIGHT: 2¼″

64. HAND SEAL: gold with a collar enamelled opalescent white on a *guilloché* ground and decorated with foliate sprays painted in sanguine enamel edged by rings of rose diamonds. The top of the seal is set with faceted topaz quartz engraved with flower sprays.
   SIGNED: M. Π.
   HEIGHT: 3½″

FOB SEALS

65. SWIVEL SEAL: cornelian and carved red and green gold.
   SIGNED: M. Π.
   HEIGHT: 2⅛″
   WIDTH: 1¾″

Left: No. 65; *Right:* No. 66

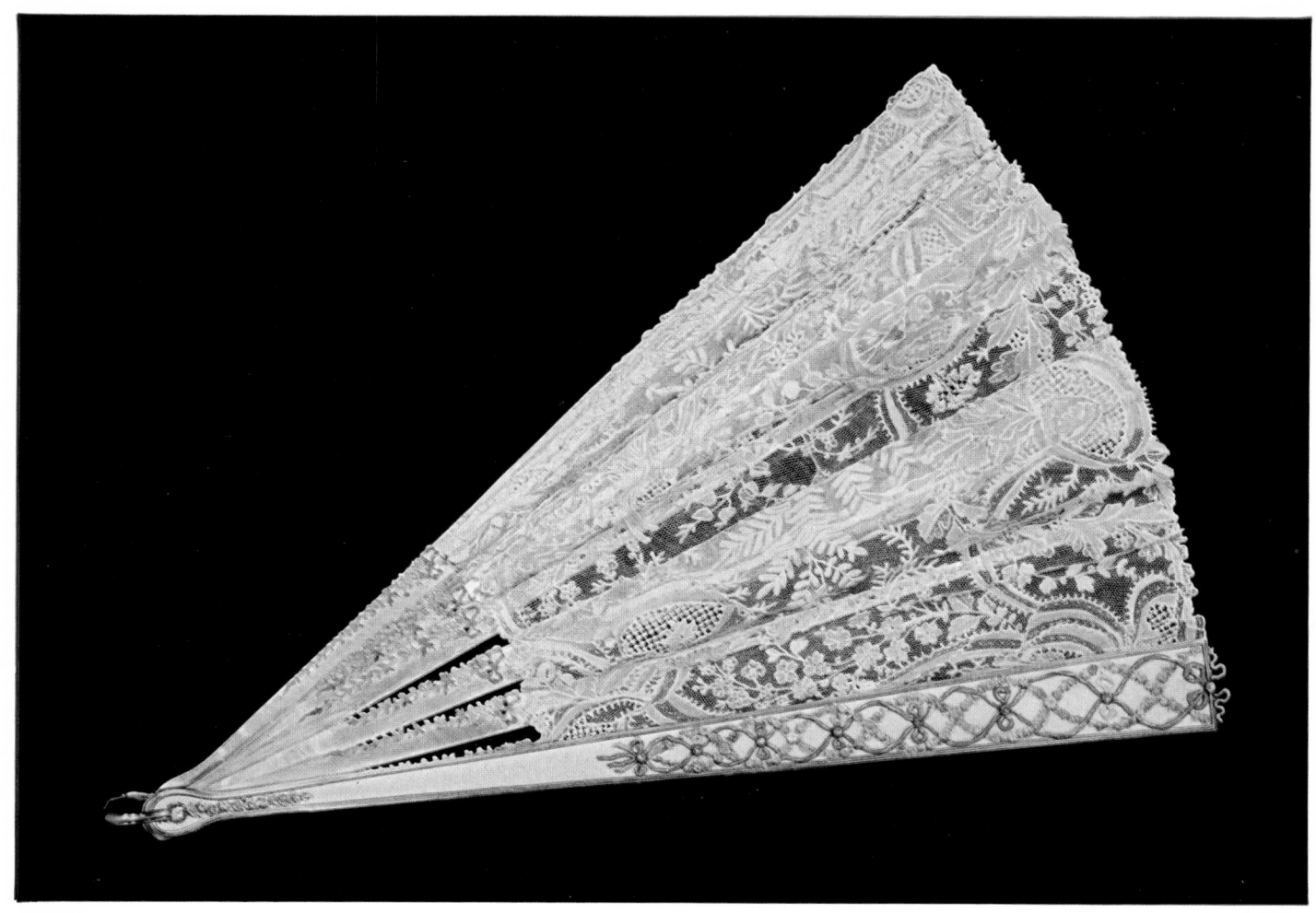

No. 75   NEEDLEPOINT LACE FAN

66. IMPERIAL SWIVEL SEAL: nephrite and carved red and green gold.
   SIGNED: H. W.
   HEIGHT: 1⅜″
   WIDTH: 1⅝″

67. WHITE ONYX SWIVEL SEAL: gold mount designed in the Etruscan manner.
   SIGNED: E. K.
   HEIGHT: 1⅝″

68. CIRCULAR SWIVEL SEAL IN PERSIAN LAPIS LAZULI: gold mount designed in the Etruscan manner.
   SIGNED: E. K.
   HEIGHT: 1⅛″

BELL PUSH

69. SQUARE BELL PUSH: Siberian jade with laurel swags carved in silver-gilt and a border in an oriental acanthus pattern. Equipped with a moonstone push, the bell is supported by four fluted bun feet.
   SIGNED: A. Г.
   2″ x 2″ x 1″

PAPER KNIVES

70. PAPER KNIFE: silver-gilt enamelled translucent deep red on a wave patterned ground. Embellished with two laurel bands, the knife is mounted with a flattened globular knob set with a rose diamond.
   SIGNED: M. П.
   LENGTH: 8⅜″

71. BOOK MARKER AND PAPER CUTTER: rock crystal mounted with gold in two colors. The blade is mounted with a gold clip and is enamelled opalescent white over an engraved ground and decorated with a ruby flower with rose diamond leaves.
   SIGNED: M. П.
   LENGTH: 3⅛″
   From the collection of the Duchess of Kent.

WHISTLE

72. WHISTLE: gold enamelled translucent pink over a wavy *guilloché* ground.
   LENGTH: 1⅜″

NOTE CASE

73. NOTE CASE: red gold with laurel borders carved in green gold and stripes enamelled in opaque white and pale pink. The front is set with a plaque enamelled opalescent white and mounted with the Imperial eagle in rose diamonds. The eagle is framed by a border of half-pearls which is suspended from a swag motif in vari-colored golds and pearls.

Originally in the Balletta Collection.
HEIGHT: 2⅛″
WIDTH: 1¹³⁄₁₆″

FAN

74. GOLD-MOUNTED FAN: the sticks are enamelled translucent coral with dark sepia plant designs against a *guilloché* field and set with brilliant and rose diamonds. The painted antique French fan itself is mounted on pierced mother-of-pearl sticks inlaid with gold.

Originally in the Balletta Collection.
SIGNED: A. H.
LENGTH: 13¾″

75. NEEDLEPOINT LACE FAN: sticks in engraved red gold enamelled opalescent white. The sticks are decorated with loops of flowers chiseled in gold of four colors which are intertwined with engraved gold ribbons and bows enamelled translucent pale blue and set with rose diamonds. The pinion is set with brilliant diamonds, and the mother-of-pearl blades are inlaid with sprays of flowers in pierced gold of four colors.

SIGNED: M. П.
GOLD MARK: crossed anchors
LENGTH: 13¾″

PRESENTATION BROOCH

76. PRESENTATION BROOCH: gold enamelled translucent green set with a spray of berries in diamonds and cabochon rubies and decorated with a gold lyre beneath a diamond Imperial crown. The brooch is further embellished with a pear-shaped brilliant pendant diamond which is suspended on a gold chain.

SIGNED: M. П.
HEIGHT: 2¹⁄₁₆″

MINIATURE EGG PENDANTS

77. THIRTEEN MINIATURE EASTER EGGS: a series of gold eggs in translucent enamels and set with various stones suspended from the branches of a silver-gilt tree of recent manufacture which rises from a piece of amethyst matrix.

TABLE CLOCKS

78. **CLOCK IN THE FORM OF A CLASSICAL TEMPLE**: Siberian nephrite decorated with red gold mounts embellished with acanthus leaves and laurel swags carved in green gold and set with five cabochon rubies. The dial is set against a panel of sun-ray pattern enamelled translucent red and edged by a bezel in red gold enamelled opaque white.

    SIGNED: H. W.

    HEIGHT: $4\frac{1}{8}''$

79. **LAPIS LAZULI CLOCK**: the dial, enamelled opalescent pale rose, is set within a foliate border of green gold which is interrupted by four rosettes of red gold edged by lines in opaque white enamel. The sides are decorated with wreaths of similar design. The dial in sun-ray pattern bears the name FABERGE in black enamel.

    SIGNED: H. W.

    $2\frac{5}{8}''$ x $1\frac{13}{16}''$ x $1\frac{1}{2}''$

80. **STRUT CLOCK**: chalcedony and silver-gilt with floral mounts in gold of four colors and a framed miniature. This clock was originally the property of Princess Albert of Saxe-Altenburg whose likeness, dated 1891, was painted by J. Zehngraf (a German miniature painter who did a number of portraits for Fabergé). The clock itself is stamped with the date 1891—a very unusual feature in Fabergé pieces.

    SIGNED: M. П.

    HEIGHT: 6''

    WIDTH: $4\frac{1}{2}''$

81. **STRUT CLOCK**: red and green gold with a border of carved acanthus leaves, enamelled translucent pink on an engraved striped background. The ivory-backed clock is further embellished with floral swags. Set within a ring of half-pearls, the dial is fitted with gold hands.

    SIGNED: H. W.

    HEIGHT: $5\frac{3}{8}''$

    WIDTH: $3\frac{1}{4}''$

FRAMES

82. **TRIANGULAR MINIATURE FRAME**: Siberian nephrite mounted with diamonds in the form of an Imperial Romanoff eagle above a bow motif centered by a ruby. The diamond-framed miniature is suspended from the bow and represents Czar

Nicholas II in full dress uniform beneath two finely *cisélé* floral sprays in gold of three colors. The miniature is backed by ivory and the strut made of gold.

The object which was originally in the Balletta Collection bears traces of Michael Perchin's initials.

HEIGHT: $5\frac{1}{2}''$

83. MINIATURE FRAME: engraved red gold enamelled opalescent white and surmounted by the Imperial crown. Framed by rose diamonds, the oval miniature painting of Marie Feodorovna, wife of Alexander III, is signed by I. Geftler, a German miniaturist from St. Petersburg.

SIGNED: H. W.
HEIGHT: $2\frac{5}{16}''$

FLOWERS

84. DANDELION ''SEEDCLOCK'': green gold with two carved nephrite leaves, strands of asbestos fibre, spun platinum and rose diamonds. The dandelion is set in a pot of carved rock crystal.

HEIGHT: $5\frac{3}{4}''$

85. SPRING WILD FLOWERS: toned chalcedony and Siberian jade with gold stalks and set with rubies. The flowers are placed in a jar of carved rock crystal.

HEIGHT: $4\frac{3}{4}''$

86. DAISIES: diamond-set petals in red gold with centers enamelled translucent bright yellow on a *repoussé* ground, with the sepals and stalks in yellow gold. The pot is carved in rock crystal.

HEIGHT: $4\frac{1}{4}''$

87. SPRAY OF FOUR WILD FLOWERS: set with two rubies, an emerald, and an amethyst, and carved in translucent quartz. The stalk is of engraved gold with a carved jade leaf rising from a white quartzite vase filled with gold moss.

SIGNED: H. W.
GOLD MARK: 72
HEIGHT: $5\frac{7}{8}''$

88. RASPBERRIES: in rhodonite (orletz) and chrysoprase with leaves carved in dark Siberian nephrite and the stalks in engraved red gold. The vase is carved rock crystal.

HEIGHT: $6''$

No. 90
Basket of Lilies of the Valley

89. CORNFLOWERS: pale gold with blue enamel heads set with small brilliant diamonds and engraved stalks and buds, set in a carved rock crystal pot.

HEIGHT: 8″

90. BASKET OF LILIES OF THE VALLEY: the flowers are of oriental pearls with leaves carved in nephrite, set in moss of rough gold. The basket is made of plaited gold wire and has a looped gold handle.

From the collection of the Duchess of Kent.

SIGNED: M. Π.

HEIGHT: 3¼″

SCULPTURE

91. GYPSY WOMAN: aventurine quartz hands and face with eyes in brilliant diamonds, a purpurine headdress, hair and shoes in black Siberian jasper; the shirt is of mottled green stone, the skirt of nephrite, and the paisley shawl in figured red-brown Ural marble. The earrings are gold and the coins silver.

This carving is a portrait of Vara Panina, a celebrated gypsy singer. The extraordinary range and beauty of her voice kept audiences entranced nightly at Moscow's *tzigane Restaurant Yar* in spite of her extreme ugliness. A vic-

tim of unrequited love for a member of the Imperial Guard, she took poison and died on the stage in front of him singing, "My heart is breaking."

HEIGHT: 7″

92. COACHMAN: face and hands are in aventurine quartz, the hair and beard in obsidian, and the coat in lapis lazuli. The hat of dull black slate is carved with the initial I for *Isvoschik*, the Russian word for coachman. The buttons are of gold, as is the belt which is painted in green, blue, yellow, mauve, pink and white enamels.

HEIGHT: 3⅝″

93. BUST OF THE UNKNOWN WARRIOR: a portrait of the legendary Russian figure skillfully carved in topaz quartz to render the textures of skin, chainmail and helmet.

HEIGHT: 6½″

94. POLAR BEAR: set with rubies for eyes, the bear is carved from rock crystal and is standing on an ice floe of the same material.

LENGTH OF BEAR: 3½″

LENGTH OF ICE FLOE: 6″

No. 91
Gypsy Woman

No. 92   COACHMAN

95. HIPPOPOTAMUS : carved from grey Kalgan jasper with rose diamond eyes set in yellow gold.

Formerly in the collection of Prince Paul of Yugoslavia.

Length: $4\frac{7}{8}''$

96. CHARGING RHINOCEROS : carved in warm mauve-grey chalcedony set with cabochon rubies for eyes.

Length: $1\frac{5}{8}''$

97. RHINOCEROS : carved in green bloodstone with an ivory horn and with cabochon rubies set in yellow gold for eyes.

Length: $4\frac{3}{4}''$

98. BISON : carved from obsidian with the surface in a mat finish except for the brightly polished muzzle, horns and hooves.

Height: $3''$

Length: $5\frac{1}{8}''$

99. HIPPOPOTAMUS : carved from pale green bowenite with gold-set ruby eyes.

Length: $2\frac{1}{8}''$

No. 101 Crouching Frog

100. SEATED ELEPHANT : carved in obsidian with rose diamond eyes.

From the collection of the Duchess of Kent.

Length: $2\frac{1}{2}''$

101. CROUCHING FROG : carved in jadeite with gold-set rose diamond eyes.

From the collections of Lady De Gray (Marchioness of Ripon) and Lady Juliet Duff.

Height: $3\frac{9}{16}''$

No. 98   Bison

No. 107 Sow

No. 103   IBIS

102. TORTOISE: the body carved from grey Kalgan jasper, the shell from figured agate, and set with rubies for eyes.
LENGTH: 2¼″

103. IBIS: vari-colored agate with carved gold legs and bill, set with rose diamond eyes. The bird is supported by an ebony base.
HEIGHT: 2¾″

104. SWAN: a large baroque pearl profusely set with rose diamonds. The beak is carved in obsidian; the eyes are cabochon rubies.
Originally in the Balletta Collection.
LENGTH: 2⅜″

105. DORMOUSE: carved in grey chalcedony and set with rose diamonds for eyes, the mouse is squatting on its haunches with the tail coiled around its hind feet and the paws held to its mouth.
From the collection of the Duchess of Kent.
LENGTH: 1¾″

106. RAM: carved in vari-colored chalcedony set with opals for eyes.
LENGTH: 2¼″

107. SOW: carved in aventurine quartz with cabochon ruby eyes.
LENGTH: 5″

108. SPANIEL PUPPY: carved from vari-colored opal with the face somewhat darker and set with cabochon ruby eyes.
LENGTH: 1⅜″

109. CAT: carved in vari-colored agate with olivine eyes.
HEIGHT: 2 1/16″

110. MOUSE: carved in vari-colored agate with cabochon ruby eyes.
LENGTH: 1¼″